E $11.93
Mo   Moncure, Jane Belk
             Word Bird's
             school words

DATE DUE			
JA 16 '90	OC 30 '9	AG 13 '92	MAR 21 '98
FE 1 '90	DE 4 '9	SE 1 '92	JAN 06 '98
FE 19 '90	JA 17 '9	AG 4 '93	OCT 15 '98
MR 20 '90	AP 16 '9	SE 3 '93	JUL 07 '9
AP 24 '90	JE 17 '91	JUL 14 '94	AUG 04 '97
JE 8 '90	JY 5 '91	AUG 8 '90	AUG 21 '9
JE 28 '90	JY 22 '9	OCT 17 '9	SEP 17 '9
JY 13 '90	AG 12 '90	DEC 15 '9	NOV 20 '9
JY 28 '90	SE 21 '9	FE 6 '90	JY 27 0
AG 21 '90	SE 10 '9	JUL 1 '1	AG 02 '0
AG 29 '90	JY 9 '92	JUL 27 '95	AG 04 '0
OC 11 '90	JY 23 '9	JAN 25 '9	SE 12 05
			JE 12 05
			JY 26 '06

JE 20 12

WORD BIRD'S SCHOOL WORDS

by Jane Belk Moncure

illustrated by Linda Hohag
and Lori Jacobson

THE CHILD'S WORLD

ELGIN, ILLINOIS 60121

Distributed by Childrens Press
Chicago, Illinois

Library of Congress Cataloging in Publication Data

Moncure, Jane Belk.
  Word Bird's school words / by Jane Belk Moncure ; illustrated by
Linda Hohag.
     p. cm. — (Word house words for early birds)
  Summary: Word Bird puts words about school in his word house,
introducing such words as "teacher," "school bus," "books," and
others.
  ISBN 0-89565-510-1
  1. Vocabulary—Juvenile literature.   2. Schools—Juvenile
literature.   [1. Schools.   2. Vocabulary.]   I. Hohag, Linda, ill.
II. Title.   III. Series: Moncure, Jane Belk.   Word house words for
early birds.
PE1449.M5296   1989
428.1—dc20   89-7179
                                                        CIP
© 1989 The Child's World, Inc.   AC
Elgin, IL
All rights reserved. Printed in U.S.A.

1 2 3 4 5 6 7 8 9 10 11 12 R 99 98 97 96 95 94 93 92 91 90 89

WORD BIRD'S
SCHOOL WORDS

Word Bird made a...

word house.

"I will put school words
in my house," he said.

He put in these words—

school clothes

school supplies

school friends

school bus

safety patrol

teacher

backpack

lockers

building blocks

play store

paints

puzzles

library

books

story

20

puppets

pets

field trip

lunchtime

games

music

marching

playground

recess

school
clothes

lockers

school
supplies

building
blocks

school
friends

play store

school
bus

paints

safety
patrol

puzzles

teacher

backpack

library

vords with  ?

lunchtime

books

games

story

music

puppets

marching

pets

playground

field trip

recess

31

You can make a school word house. You can put Word Bird's words in your house and read them too.

Can you think of other school words to put in your word house?